A special thanks
to everyone
who has helped make
Know Yourself
what it is today.

Dear Reader

Knowing yourself is truly the beginning of all wisdom. We give young learners the building blocks they need to start their unique journey of self-discovery: an understanding of human anatomy — literally how we are put together. Knowledge of one's own human body is an empowering context on which anyone can build.

Learning about the body and mind at a young age sets the foundation for honoring one's physical form, develops confidence, and begins the discovery of who we are meant to be.

Now that's real power.

The Know Yourself Team

Quick-Start Guide

Hello Know Yourselfers!

Follow these steps to start a new journey and explore the renal system. Have fun on this quest and remember - keep the information flowing!

1

Grab a clay tablet and some walnuts! We are going to Ancient Assyria.

You won't find Assyria on your map, look for Syria and Iraq on your atlas, or find an online map of the world.

2

Read Time Skaters Adventure 4.

Pinky and Shorty run up against the law of Queen Serimamis. The perils of Babylon will require all their cunning.

3

Get equipped!

Gather your supplies and prepare for your activities. It's time for you to make your own wonders.

Table of Contents

Hello Adventurer!

Welcome to Adventure 4 - The Renal System.

In this workbook, you will learn about Ancient Assyria and your body's Renal System. There will be information to read, activities to complete, and quizzes to take when you are ready to challenge yourself! Take your time along the way - spend as much or as little time as you like on each activity.

Good luck, and have fun!

Destination: Ancient Assyria!

THE TIME TRAVEL CLOCK READS

810 BCE

Get ready
to clean things up!

NINEVEH

ANCIENT ASSYRIA

ASSUR

EUPHRATES RIVER

BABYLON

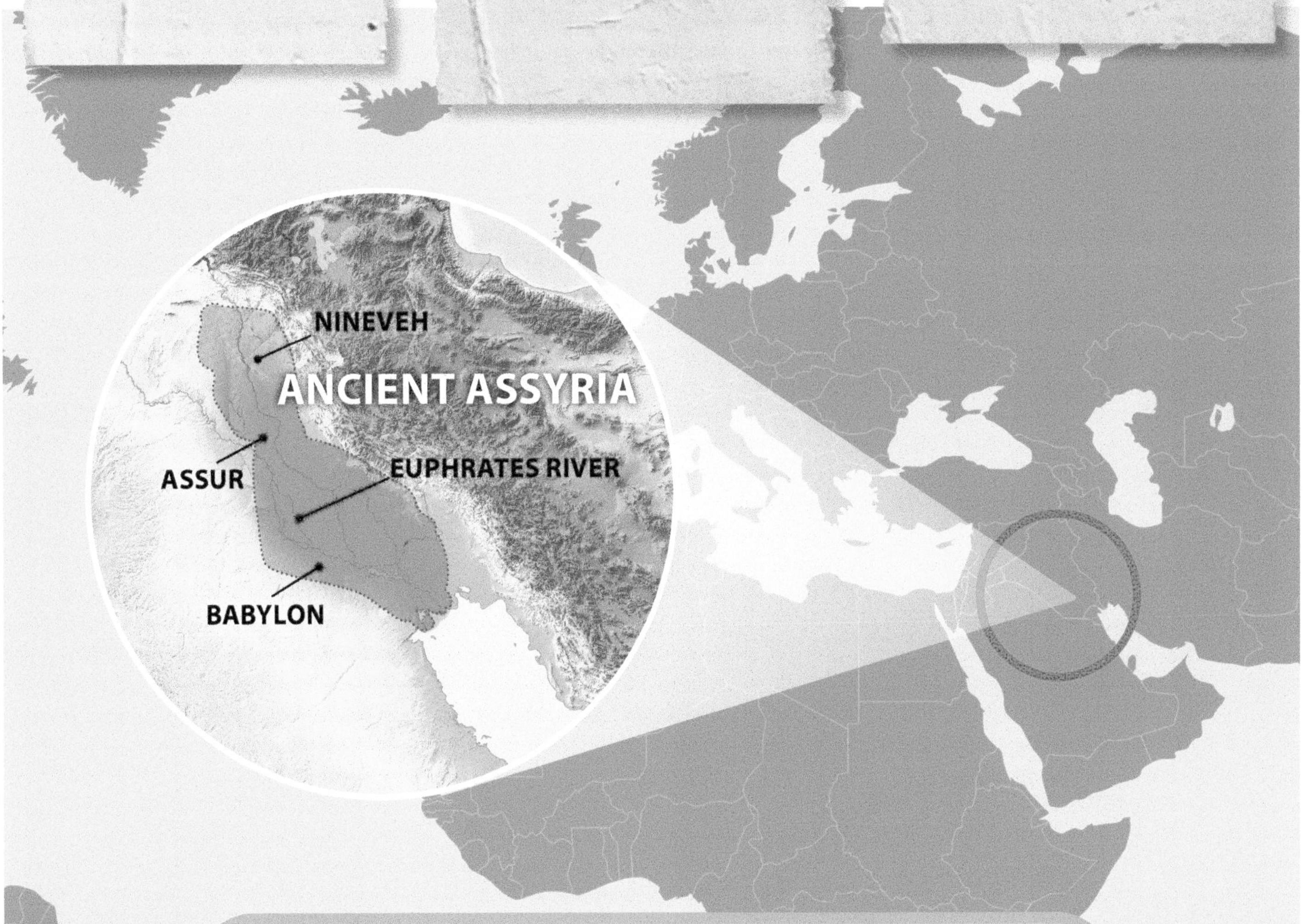

Join us along the Euphrates.*

The Euphrates was an important water source for the people of ancient Assyria.

*Say it like this: "you-FRAY-tees"

The strongest syllable is shown in CAPITALS and red.

Let's enter this portal for....

Time Skaters Adventure 4: You've Got to be Kidney!

WHAT DO WE DO?

HAAAANK!!

YES, YES, WHAT IS IT?

OH!

RUN TOWARDS THAT PORTAL!

MY APOLOGIES, LADIES...

THAT WAS THE NILE RIVER I TRANSPORTED YOU TO, NOT THE EUPHRATES. SIMPLE MISCALCULATION ON MY PART.

THE RENAL SYSTEM

SHORTY... WHAT HAPPENED? ARE YOU OK?

EL-BIDNAM, WHY WERE THESE TWO YOUNG GIRLS BROUGHT HERE?

CLEARLY THEY MEANT NO HARM.

THAT MAY BE SO, BUT THEY STILL BROKE THE LAW. SINCE THE WATER SUPPLY IS UNDER OUR CONTROL, IT'S IMPORTANT WE REINFORCE THE RULES.

PUNISHING THESE CHILDREN WILL DO NOTHING BUT CAUSE MORE PANIC AND FEAR.

HAVE THE SERVANTS PREPARE CHAMBERS FOR THEM. I'D LIKE THEM TO STAY AT THE PALACE AS MY GUESTS.

AS YOU WISH, YOUR HIGHNESS.

CAN YOU BELIEVE IT? YOU HAVE TO PAY TO USE THE WATER HERE.

HOW DID YOU HEAR THAT?

SOMETHING'S NOT RIGHT, HANK?

MY SCANNERS ARE SHOWING THE EUPHRATES IS FULL OF POLLUTANTS. SO WHILE THERE IS WATER, THERE IS A SHORTAGE OF CLEAN WATER.

THE RENAL SYSTEM

coloring
opportunity

Learning Calendar

Part 1

Know Your History

Estimated hours **6** *hours of fun*

Locate Ancient Assyria on the map on page 1 or using a globe, atlas, or an online map (like this one: https://knowyourself.com/maps)

Read the comic **Time Skaters Adventure 4: You've Got to be Kidney!** Find it at the beginning of this Adventure Guide!

Gather the adventure equipment you'll need from around the house - find the checklist on pages 24-27!

Enlighten yourself in *Know Your History*.

Decipher ancient languages in *Know Your Script*.

Make *Your Mark* in Ancient Assyrian Script.

Discover the *Mystery of the Hanging Gardens of Babylon*.

Create *Your Creature* and show the world what lurks within.

Crack the *Ancient Assyria Crossword*.

Don't *Make a Mess(opotamia)* - put your knowledge to the test!

Part 2

Know Your Renal System

Examine purification in *Know Your Renal System*.

Confront *Separation Anxiety*.

Turn the old into new while in *Need of Nephrons*.

Filter with friends as a *Potent Processor*.

Solve the *Renal Rumble*.

Uncover the *Kidneys' Claim to Fame!*

Part **3**

Know Your Appetite

Feast your eyes on *Know Your Appetite*.

Review the recipes. Make a Shopping List. Get your Kitchen Ready.

Fix up some *Tahini Hummus* and *Walnut Butter Cookies*.

Share your dishes with your family. Discuss *Thoughts for Young Chefs* around the table!

Part **4**

Show What You Know!

Take some time to *Babble On about Babylon*.

Check out *Further Reading* for more opportunities to learn.

Great job on all your hard work!

Home Inventory Checklist

Ask your parents to help you find these items around the house. These are some of the tools you will need on your adventure.

> Don't worry if you can't find every single item - just use your imagination to find substitutions!

- ☐ **Newspaper**
  - Mystery of the Hanging Gardens of Babylon

- ☐ **A small pot, jar, or a recycled container**
  - Mystery of the Hanging Gardens of Babylon

- ☐ **Dirt**
  - Mystery of the Hanging Gardens of Babylon

- ☐ **Plant seeds or a seedling**
  - Mystery of the Hanging Gardens of Babylon

- ☐ **Pencil, pen or markers**
  - Create Your Creature

- ☐ **Paper**
  - Create Your Creature

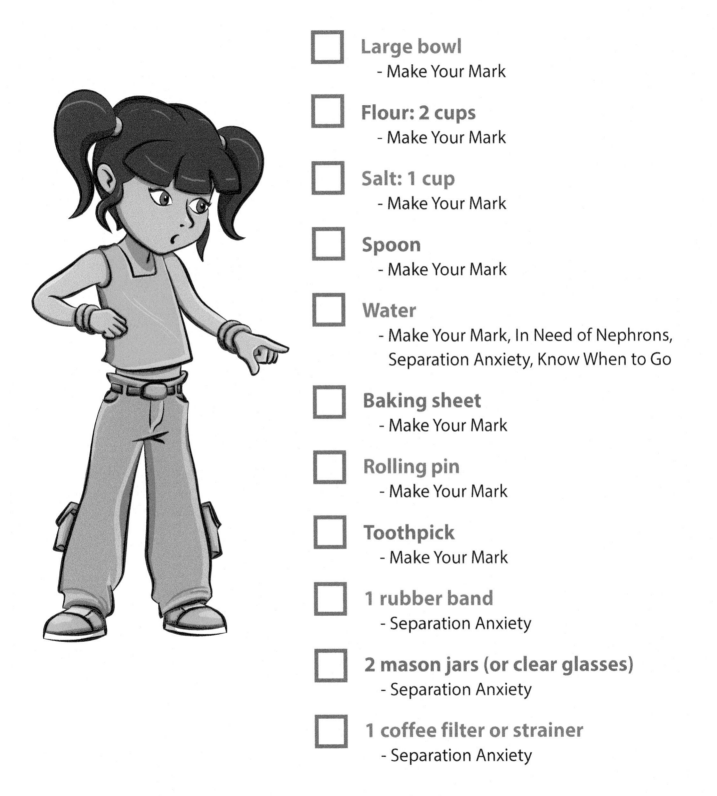

☐ **Large bowl**
  - Make Your Mark

☐ **Flour: 2 cups**
  - Make Your Mark

☐ **Salt: 1 cup**
  - Make Your Mark

☐ **Spoon**
  - Make Your Mark

☐ **Water**
  - Make Your Mark, In Need of Nephrons, Separation Anxiety, Know When to Go

☐ **Baking sheet**
  - Make Your Mark

☐ **Rolling pin**
  - Make Your Mark

☐ **Toothpick**
  - Make Your Mark

☐ **1 rubber band**
  - Separation Anxiety

☐ **2 mason jars (or clear glasses)**
  - Separation Anxiety

☐ **1 coffee filter or strainer**
  - Separation Anxiety

Home Inventory Checklist

(continuation)

- [ ] **1 cup of small pebbles (the size of fish tank gravel)**
  - Separation Anxiety

- [ ] **1 paper towel**
  - Separation Anxiety, In Need of Nephrons

- [ ] **1 tablespoon of food coloring or apple juice**
  - Separation Anxiety

- [ ] **10 items to use as tokens**
  - Potent Processor

- [ ] **A 6 sided die**
  - Potent Processor

- [ ] **A cup or small bowl**
  - In Need of Nephrons

- [ ] **Vinegar**
  - In Need of Nephrons

- [ ] **Cotton rope (about 8 yards total)**
  - Knot Your Average Garden

- [ ] **Measuring tape**
  - Knot Your Average Garden

- [ ] **Scissors**
  - Knot Your Average Garden

- [ ] **A large key ring (or wooden rings if you one on hand)**
  - Knot Your Average Garden
- [ ] **Potted plant from the Mystery of the Hanging Gardens of Babylon activity**
  - Knot Your Average Garden
- [ ] **A ceiling hook**
  - Knot Your Average Garden
- [ ] **A balloon or 2 (in case the first gets too full)**
  - Know When to Go
- [ ] **Straw**
  - Know When to Go

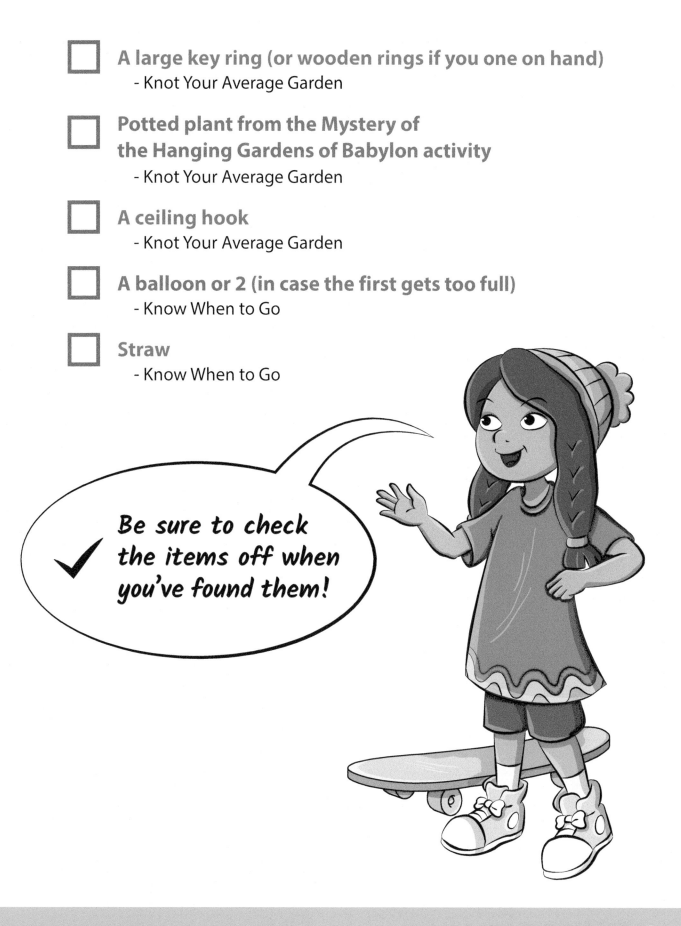

Be sure to check the items off when you've found them!

Know Your History

Ancient Assyria is really really really old! It's one of the first civilizations (also an empire) that we know inhabited Mesopotamia, "**the country between two rivers**." According to many historians, ancient Assyria boasts many "firsts," including one of the first studies of geometry, one of the first advanced banking systems, the first writing system (called cuneiform), and the first documented recipes written on clay tablets all the way back in the 18th century BCE!

TIGRIS RIVER

EUPHRATES RIVER

BABYLON

Located where the Tigris and Euphrates rivers run close to each other was the city of Babylon, famous for **The Hanging Gardens of Babylon**. One of "The Seven Wonders of the Ancient World," the gardens are considered something between history and myth.

Described as spectacular and lush, the gardens would have required a complicated irrigation system — Greek historian Diodorus wrote that they were 400 feet wide by 400 feet long and over 80 feet high! Although the gardens are not in Babylonian historical documents, their construction could've been possible with the technology of the time. Until we find more physical evidence, this Wonder lives on in ancient texts and works of art.

Know Your History

Queen Sammu-Ramat (also know as **Semiramis**), one of the world's first female leaders, briefly ruled Assyria around the turn of the 8th century BCE. She served as the empress of Assyria during the time after her husband's death and before her son became old enough to take over the kingdom.

In general, women were not in positions of authority during the Assyrian Empire, so it was quite an accomplishment for Queen Sammu-Ramat to take the throne and maintain her position of power.

Historical records are not clear, but legends say that Assyria thrived during her reign, and that she was responsible for many construction projects, including complex irrigation systems for agriculture.

Know Your Script

Ancient Assyrians spoke several languages, but they wrote in **cuneiform**, which is one of the earliest writing systems. The name comes from the literal translation of the Latin words cuneus, or "wedge," and forma, or "shape."

Unlike the letters of the Roman alphabet, the one we use, each series of shapes was originally based on a picture of the object or animal it represents. Over time, these pictures developed into wedge-shaped marks.

Instead of paper, Assyrians carved them on clay tablets, most of which fit in the palm of their hand. They were probably a lot heavier than the "tablets" you're used to!

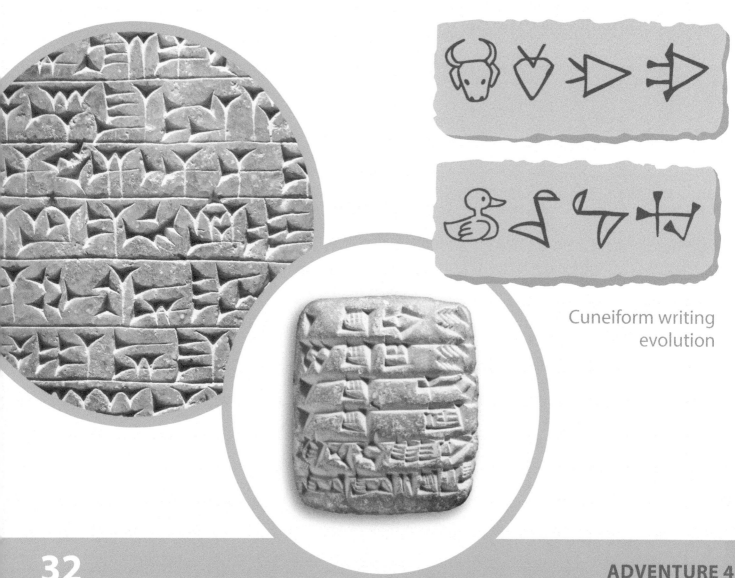

Cuneiform writing evolution

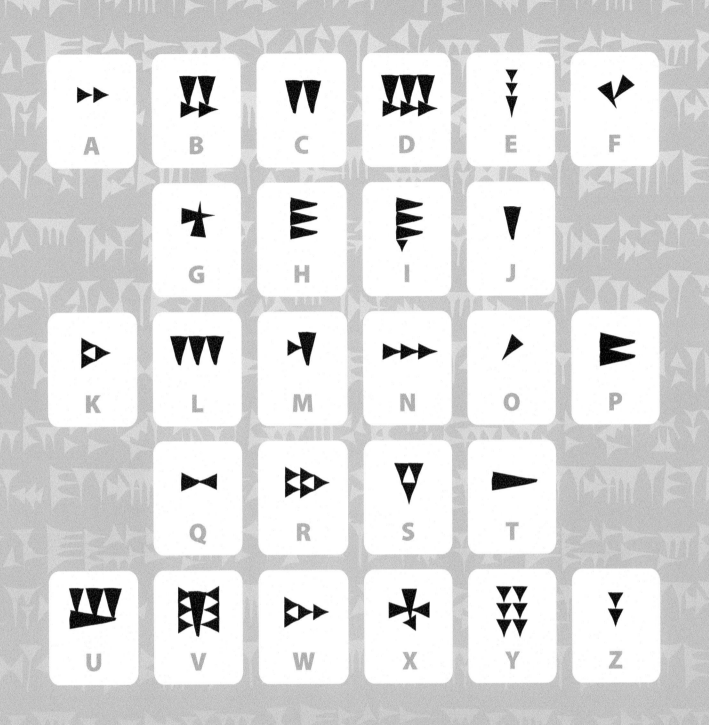

Using the alphabet guide, decipher this message:

_____

Make Your Mark

Cuneiform clay tablets recorded business items and activities, but often told myths and stories as well. **Make your mark like an Ancient Assyrian!**

Use home inventory materials and directions on the next pages to make a writing tablet and record a message.

Materials:

- **Large bowl**
- **Flour: 2 cups**
- **Salt: 1 cup**
- **Spoon**
- **Water: 1 cup**
- **Baking sheet**
- **Rolling pin**
- **Toothpick**

Directions:

1. Add flour and salt into a large bowl. Stir them together using a spoon.

2. Slowly stir the water into the mixture.

3. Take both hands and press or roll the mixture down and around the sides of the bowl (this is called "kneading").

   Continue kneading for around 10 minutes until your dough gets a smooth consistency.

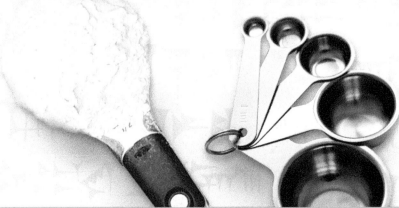

Make Your Mark

4. Roll the dough into a ball. Allow the dough to harden a little by letting the mix rest for 15 minutes.

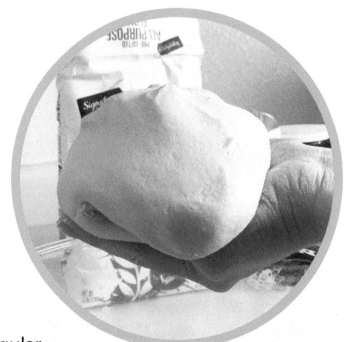

5. Roll your dough out into a rectangular tablet shape, you can use a rolling pin or anything flat to help. Roll out onto a baking sheet for easy transport to the oven later.

   Note: If your dough is too hard to roll, add a little sprinkle of water. If it is too soft, let it rest a bit longer.

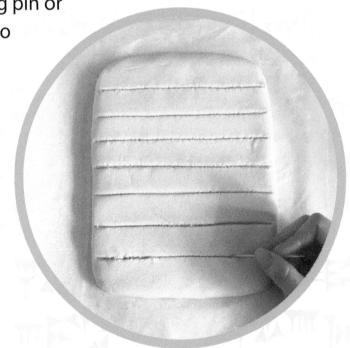

6. Once you have a tablet rolled out (a half-inch to an inch in thickness), make your mark in Ancient Assyrian cuneiform using a toothpick. If your dough gets a little too hard while you are marking your script try spreading a few droplets of water onto your cuneiform tablet using your fingers.

7. **You will need an adult for this baking step!**

To finish, bake your project in the oven at 250 degrees fahrenheit for 3 or more hours (poke with a fork to check if it can be punctured easily at the bottom, if so- keep baking). Allow your project to cool completely before moving it anywhere else. This could take another hour or so!

Note: You can replace making your own dough with playdoh if you have some available!

Mystery of the Hanging Gardens of Babylon

Wondering what's up with the **"Hanging" Gardens of Babylon?** If so, you're not alone! Researchers have long tried to unravel the mysteries of this ancient wonder.

Studies of ancient text may be the reason for the mixup. One point of confusion is the geographical location of Babylon itself. Researchers now believe they have pinpointed this seventh wonder of the world to Nineveh — a city located in Northern Assyria. Arabic sources note that this northern Assyrian city was widely known as "Old Babylon," while Didorus Siculus writings describe Babylonian palaces in detail that resemble those that contemporaneously existed in Nineveh.

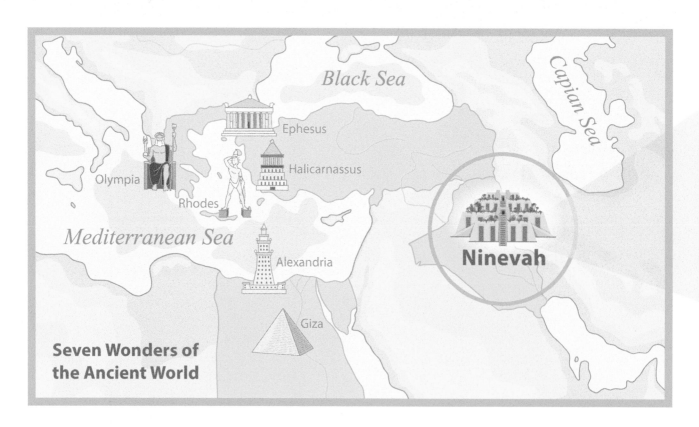

Black Sea

Capian Sea

Ephesus

Halicarnassus

Olympia

Rhodes

Mediterranean Sea

Ninevah

Alexandria

Giza

Seven Wonders of the Ancient World

Another of the Hanging Gardens of Babylon's many mysteries is what the garden actually looked like. Based on the English translation of the word **"hanging"**, one may think of plants or foliage dangling from the ceiling. However, the true Greek translation of the word for hanging is "Kremastos", which means to create an upward, raised slope. By that definition, the dirt piling on the plant root system to create a mound could be what the Ancient Assyrians were actually referring to!

Not lost in translation is the decorative beauty and spectacular utility of the Gardens. Plants, shrubs, and trees provided shade from the sun, and supplied fruit and herbal medicines.

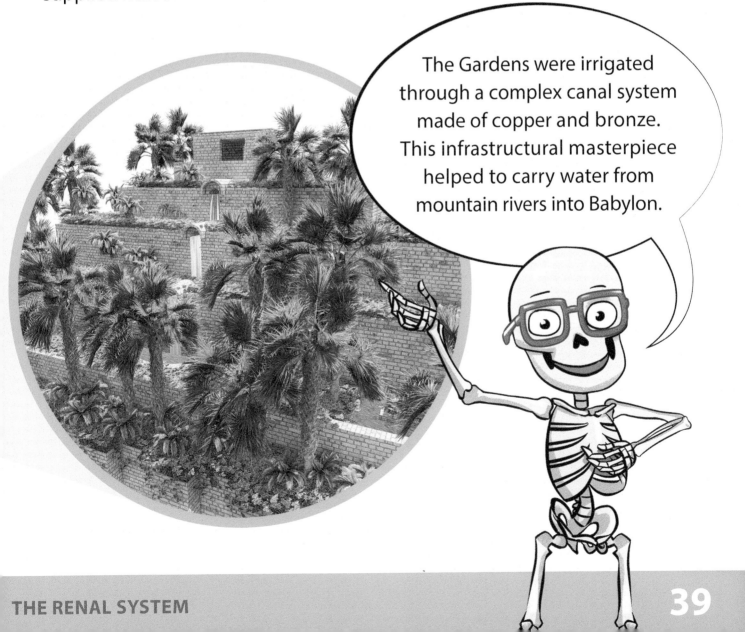

The Gardens were irrigated through a complex canal system made of copper and bronze. This infrastructural masterpiece helped to carry water from mountain rivers into Babylon.

Mystery of the Hanging Gardens of Babylon

The Hanging Gardens of Babylon were created in the image of the Northwestern Assyrian Mountains.

What plants are native to your area?

Try making your version of the Hanging Gardens of Babylon using a native plant and the gardening directions on the next page - have fun!

Materials:

- **Newspaper**
- **A small pot, jar, or recycled container**
  (clean pasta sauce jars work great!)
- **Dirt**
- **Plant seeds or a seedling**

Directions:

1. Lay out a few sheets of newspaper as your work area.

2. Take out your small pot, jar, or container.

3. Measure how much area you will need for your seedling inside the container (skip this step if you are using seeds).

4. Add enough dirt to fill the space between the seedling and bottom of the jar, or fill the pot with dirt completely if you have seeds (leave an inch from the top for watering later on).

5. Place your seedling into the jar and fill the gaps on the sides with dirt. If you have seeds, you'll want to plant them at a depth two times the height of the seed itself.

6. Follow the directions located on your seed packet or seedling to find out how much sunlight and water your new plant needs to grow big and strong. Enjoy!

Knot Your Average Garden

This is a fun project if you still feel inspired by the Western interpretation of the Greek word for **'hanging'**. This activity will help you create the garden of your dreams that hangs from the sky (or the ceiling).

Materials:

- **Cotton rope** (about 8 yards total)

- **Measuring tape**

- **Scissors**

- **A large keyring**
  (wooden rings are great if you have one!)

- **Potted plant from the Mystery of the Hanging Gardens of Babylon activity**

- **A ceiling hook**

 Show off your skills!

Have your grown up take a photo, and share on social media using the hashtag:

#KnowYourAdventure

 KnowYourselfOAK   KnowYourselfOAK

Knot Your Average Garden

Directions:

1. Unravel your rope in a floor area with little or no foot traffic.

2. Next, take your measuring tape and note how large 70 inches is (you can use real tape or a couple of shoes to mark your dimensions on the floor).

3. Cut 4 pieces of cotton rope that are 70 inches long using your scissors.

4. Line up the strings next to one another. Then take the bundle of strings and put it through your keyring (make sure the strings are even on either side of the key ring).

5. Make your first knot to secure the strings to the keyring - this is the start of your plant hanger!

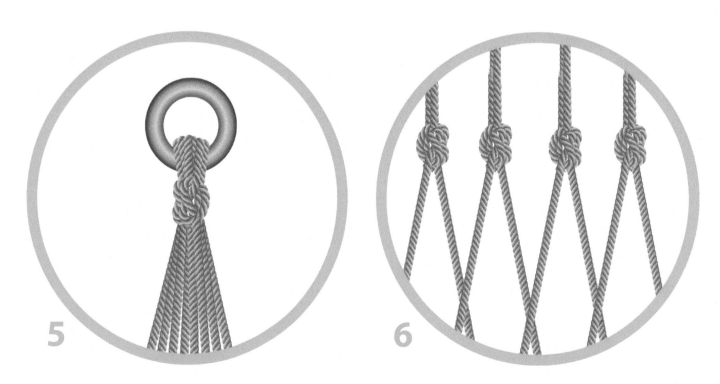

6. You should see 8 strings in front of you. Take two of the strings and form 1 knot about 12 inches from the top knot you made earlier. Repeat 3 times until you have 4 knots in total.

7. Now, form 4 more knots (about 2 inches down) below the first group using strings that sit next to each other and are not tied together already. You are making a net that will hug your plant!

8. Lastly, form one more knot- this will secure your pot safely inside the net. Place the last knot about 3 inches down to complete the hanger.

9. **You will need an adult's help** hanging your new plant hanger. To hang the planter, you will just need a secured ceiling hook and someone to help you place your small plant carefully into the net.

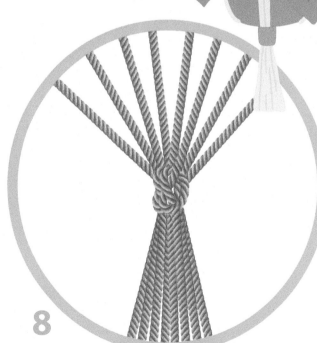

7

8

Create Your Creature

Most of the artwork that survived from the Assyrian empire is sculpture. The detailed stone carvings feature animals like horses, lions, and hawks. To guard doorways of important buildings, Assyrians sculpted huge mythical creatures — usually terrifying combinations like winged lions or birds with bearded human heads. Even if you didn't know how to read a sign, you'd understand the warning of a giant lion head!

Can you make your own mythical creature? Write down the names of 4 animals and what makes them interesting or scary. Now take those parts, mix them together, and draw your own creature.

Here are some examples of awesome creatures and their fun features:

Animal	What Makes Them Interesting
Birds	Amazing Wings
Bull	Hardy Head
Crocodile	Powerful Bite
Goat	Strong Horns
Lion	Ferocious Roar
Snake	Poisonous Fangs
Turtle	Safe Shell

Materials:

- **Pen or pencil**
- **Paper**

Directions:

1. What does your creature's head look like? Perhaps it has the face of a snake with the mane of a lion. How about features of a goat? Goats are known for being stubborn, so the head of a goat not only gives it cool horns, but a built-in personality! Pick a head and draw it.

2. Is your creature as strong as a bull or as protected as a turtle? Pick the body of your creature and draw that.

3. How does your animal move around? The legs of a horse are swift, but the wings of a bird or a dragon allow your creature to traverse the skies! Draw some legs and wings if you'd like your creature to have either.

4. A tail is all you need to finish your creature. Dog and cat tails were popular in Assyrian art, but you can use tails they had never even heard of! How about a rattlesnake? Draw a tail for your creature.

5. Name your creature, so its legend can pass through the centuries.

Ancient Assyria Crossword

After you finish, check the answer key on page 110.

Across:

4. An important water source for the people of Ancient Assyria.

5. _____ creatures were sculpted to guard the doorways of important Ancient Assyrian buildings.

6. In Arabic sources, the Northern Assyrian city of Nineveh was widely known as Old _____.

7. A queen who ruled Assyria around the turn of the 8th Century BCE.

8. Researchers have traced the true location of the Hanging Gardens of Babylon to this northern city.

9. The Ancient Assyrian writing system.

Down:

1. A staple food in Ancient Assyria.

2. The Greek word for 'hanging'.

3. A canal system of copper and bronze cylinders helped water the Hanging Gardens of Babylon through a process called _____.

9. Tablets for recording messages were made of this material.

Don't Make a Mess(opotamia)

Good work, Adventurers!
Now that you have read some things about the history of Ancient Assyria, let's review what you have learned!

Try to fill in the blanks.

Ancient Assyria is very old, and historians believe it may have been the first place

we know of where people studied __ __ __ __ __ __ __ __ , had advanced

__ __ __ __ __ __ __ __ and even had a common system for __ __ __ __ __ __ __ __

used for things like recipes.

Mesopotamia means "the country between two rivers," because it was located

between the __ __ __ __ __ __ __ and the __ __ __ __ __ __ __ __ __ __ .

The city of Babylon was known for many things, but perhaps the most famous are

"The __ __ __ __ __ __ __ __ __ __ __ __ __ of Babylon", which were listed

among "The __ __ __ __ __ Wonders of the Ancient world," though now historians

aren't sure if they were more history or myth.

Queen __ __ __ __ __ - __ __ __ __ __ was one of the world's first known female

rulers, serving as the empress of Assyria until her __ __ __ could take over. Accord-

ing to legends, she was responsible for many __ __ __ __ __ __ __ __ __ __ __ __

projects, the remnants of which are a large part of how Assyria is studied today!

Well done, Adventurer!

You can check your answers
using the key on page 111.

Know Your Renal System

Waste Not, Want Not

Peeing—we all do it. Now, let's find out why! Pee, or urine, is produced by the urinary system, also known as the **renal system**.

Here are the parts of your renal system:

- **Kidneys:** two-bean shaped organs about the size of your fist are located on either side of your lumbar spine. They are protected by your bottom ribs. ("Renal" comes from the Latin word for "kidney.")

- **Ureters:*** thin tubes where urine travels from each kidney to the bladder.

- **Bladder:** a hollow organ—shaped like a triangle when empty and round when full—that holds urine until it's time to urinate. It's about the size of a grapefruit.

- **Urethra:*** the tube that carries urine from the bladder out of the body.

> *Say them like this:
>
> **ureters** - "YER-eh-terz"
> **urethra** - "yoo-REE-thruh"
>
> The strongest syllable is always shown in CAPITALS and red.

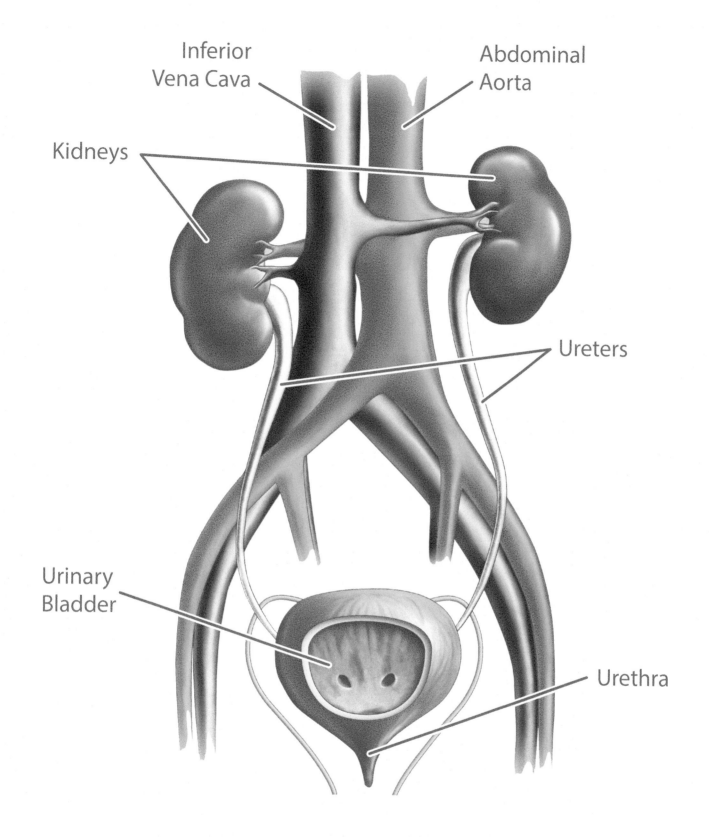

Inferior Vena Cava

Abdominal Aorta

Kidneys

Ureters

Urinary Bladder

Urethra

Fun Fact: Kidneys usually come in a pair, but you can live with just one!

Kidneys:
Your Filtration Station

Each kidney has large blood vessels that move blood into and out of it, and a ureter that carries the final waste — urine — out to the urinary bladder. The kidneys also have a lot of small blood vessels traveling through them because they filter wastes out of the blood (while keeping the good stuff like your blood cells). Your kidneys are always busy cleaning your blood.

They can cleanse all the blood in your body in about 50 minutes.

Renal Pyramids
are structures in the kidney medulla (the center of an organ) that contain millions of tubes that form and collect urine. This is where the kidney reabsorbs (takes back into the bloodstream) nutrients, certain chemicals, and water that the body wants to keep. Each kidney contains 5 to 11 renal pyramids, and about 1 million tube units.

Renal Cortex
is the outer part of the kidney (cortex means "shell"). Most of the blood entering the kidney travels through the renal cortex, where it gets filtered to remove wastes.

Renal Artery
supplies the kdney with blood from the heart.

Renal Vein
takes cleansed blood out of the kidney and back towards the heart.

Ureter
carries urine from the kidney to the urinary bladder.

Renal Pyramid:
The Journey Within

Let's zoom in on a section of a renal pyramid and the layer of the cortex above it. The working units of the kidney are made up of loops of tubes called **nephrons*** and larger tubes called collecting ducts. Each kidney has about 1 million of these units.

The journey of wastes from bloodstream to urine starts in the cortex, in a ball of tiny blood vessels (capillaries) called the **glomerulus*** which has small holes for filtration. Water and waste pass through these holes, but larger materials like blood cells stay behind in the bloodstream. The liquid leaves the glomerulus and flows on to the nephron, where nutrients, chemicals, and water that you want to keep in your body are reabsorbed (sucked back in). When the liquid arrives in the collecting duct, your body decides how much more water it wants to keep. In fact, only 1% of this liquid ends up becoming urine!

*Say them like this:

nephrons - "NEF-rons"
glomerulus - "gluh-MAIR-you-luss"

The strongest syllable is always shown in CAPITALS and red.

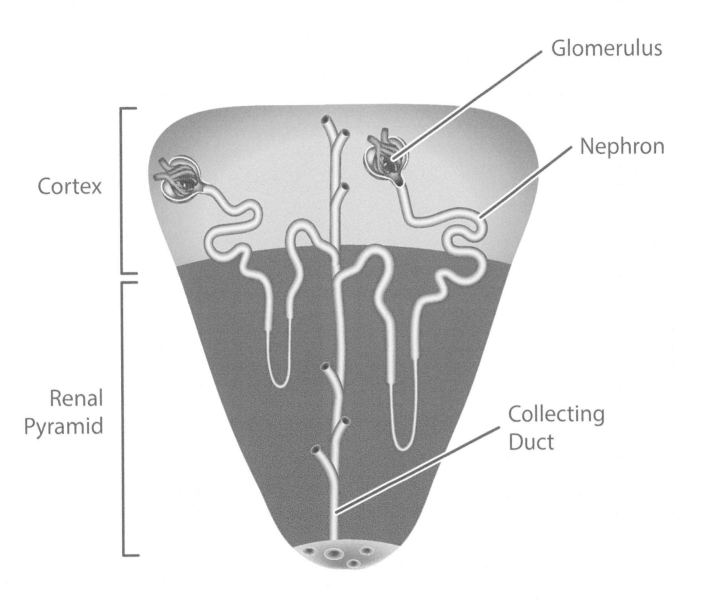

Glomerulus

Nephron

Cortex

Renal
Pyramid

Collecting
Duct

If you haven't been drinking much water,
the collecting duct reabsorbs more water back into the body,
and the urine that you excrete has a darker yellow color.

Fennec foxes have such efficient kidneys that they don't even need
to drink water. Crocodiles, on the other hand, can't concentrate
liquid at all, so their kidneys make solid waste to save water.

Know Your Kidneys:

Separation Anxiety

Your renal system takes waste and toxins out of the blood hundreds of times every day. The kidneys act as filters, separating waste from large, important materials that need to stay in the bloodstream. This activity illustrates how a human kidney removes waste from the blood.

Materials:

- **Water**

- **2 Mason jars** (or clear glasses)

- **1 cup of small pebbles** (the size of fish tank gravel)

- **1 tablespoon of food coloring or apple juice**

- **1 rubber band**

- **1 coffee filter or strainer**

- **1 paper towel**

Directions:

1. Fill the first jar halfway with warm water and mix in the pebbles and food coloring. This mixture represents the bloodstream: blood cells, waste, and everything else.

2. Use the rubber band to seal a coffee filter over the top of the second jar. This jar is your "kidney."

3. Slowly pour the fluid from the bloodstream jar into the kidney jar. The coffee filter acts like the filtration structure in your kidneys. It holds back large particles like blood cells, or in this case, pebbles, while letting most of the water and waste through. This filtered liquid will eventually become your urine.

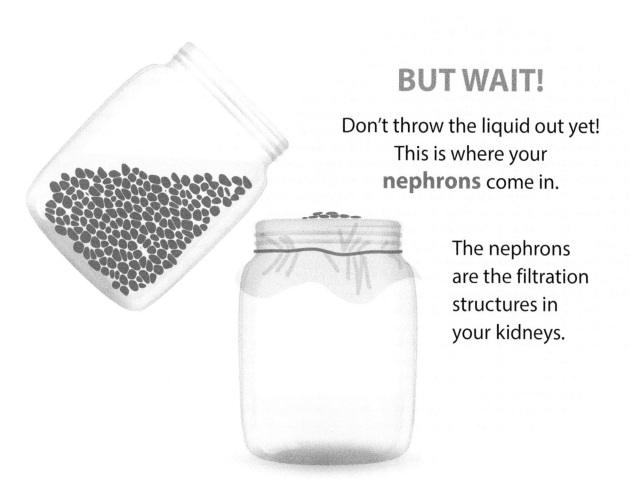

BUT WAIT!

Don't throw the liquid out yet! This is where your **nephrons** come in.

The nephrons are the filtration structures in your kidneys.

Know Your Kidneys: Separation Anxiety

When blood flows through a nephron, one part called the **glomerulus*** allows fluid and waste products to pass through it. However, the glomerulus does not let through blood cells and large molecules, like proteins.

Then, special tubes in each nephron—which you'll learn more about in the **Aha! Moment** on pages 62 and 63—pull water, chemicals, and nutrients back into your blood, allowing other materials to be sent out as waste.

4. Fold a paper towel in half, and then fold it in half again. It should be nice and thick.

5. Dip a corner of the paper towel into the liquid. Hold it there as it absorbs the colored water.

> *Say it like this:
>
> **glomerulus**
>
> "gluh-MAIR-you-luss"
>
> The strongest syllable is always shown in CAPITALS and red.

6. Now the liquid is ready to be sent out of the body as urine. Holding the wet paper towel over the sink or an empty container, gently squeeze the paper towel so some liquid drips out. That's "pee"!

This is similar to how nephrons work in your own body to reabsorb water and chemicals you want to keep, to maintain balance in your body.

Repeat the filtering process (steps 1–5) using a lower concentration of waste (the same amount of pebbles and food coloring, but more water).

Notice the liquid's color.

What can this tell you about your own urine?

If you used a higher concentration (the same amount of pebbles and water, but more food coloring),

what do you think would happen?

Why?

This Adventure's Touchstone: where anatomy, physiology, and psychology all come together.

AHA!

The Long and Winding Road

Imagine standing at a fork in the road. You must go down one path or the other. Signs tell you that one way leads to the short road, and the other leads to the long road. Which would you choose?

The benefits of the short road seem obvious. You reach your destination sooner. There might be fewer obstacles. So why would anyone take the long road?

Let's take another look at the journey blood takes through your kidneys. Blood travels through a million filtration units called **nephrons**. These remove waste and help the body absorb what it needs back into the blood. The structure of the nephrons — long and winding tubes — is important to this function.

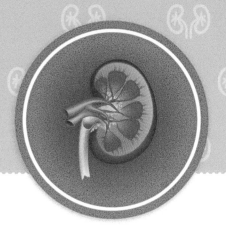

When blood goes through a nephron's **convoluted tubules***
(very twisty, small tubes), then down and up one big hairpin
turn called the **nephron loop** (or **Loop of Henle***), it might
not seem like the quickest or most direct route. But this path
is what gives the kidneys time to reabsorb essential substances,
like glucose and water (we don't want to lose all our water).

**Kidneys filter over 100 liters of fluid every
day, enough to fill an average bathtub!**

That's a lot of fluid and a lot of tubule to travel.

*Say them like this:

convoluted tubules - "kon-vo-LOO-tid TOO-byo-
ols"

Henle - "HEN-lee"
The strongest syllable is always shown in CAPITALS and red.

In Need of Nephrons

Your nephrons are the cleaning and filtration units in your blood. With the aid of millions of them, the things your body needs are reabsorbed and the things it does not need are kicked out into your bladder to get expelled.

You might not think of blood as something that can get "cleaned," but without your kidneys, you'd get very sick very quickly (it's a good thing you have two in case something goes wrong)!

Just as blood circulates through your body, currency (money) circulates through the economy. If you have ever looked at a pile of pennies, you have probably noticed that some are much dirtier than others. It would be pretty hard to wash them with soap, since part of what ages them is the copper oxide that builds up on the surface. With a bit of vinegar you can make them look as shiny as when they were new!

Materials:

- Some dirty or dull pennies

- A cup or small bowl

- Paper towels

- Water

- Vinegar

Directions:

1. Put the dirty pennies in your bowl

2. Pour just enough vinegar to cover the pennies

3. Wait for at least 10 minutes.

4. Take the pennies out and rinse them off with water, then rub them with the paper towel until they are dried off.

5. Great job - you've just acted as a kidney for your coins!

Straws and Balloons

Once the urine is in your kidney's collecting ducts, you need to get that waste out of your body. To prevent you from peeing your pants, the rest of your renal system has a way of storing urine until you can find a bathroom.

The urine travels through special tubes called ureters - each kidney has 1, and each is like a long straw (8-10 inches long) with muscles that help push the urine along. At the end of the tubes, the urine drops into the urinary bladder, which is kind of like a balloon surrounded by muscle. When urine fills the bladder, it can expand to up to 15 times its resting size until it holds up to 2 cups of urine.

Because you make between 4 and 5 cups of urine a day, you need to empty the urinary bladder several times every day.

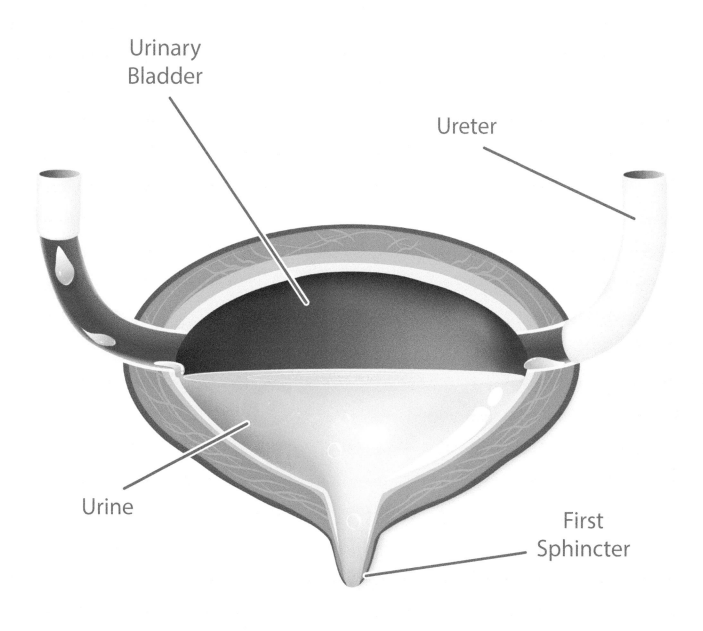

Urinary
Bladder

Ureter

Urine

First
Sphincter

When your kidneys are healthy, you make at least
1 tablespoon of urine an hour. So even when you are
sleeping and not drinking water, you still produce urine.

Know Your Flow

Urine travels from the kidney and then is stored in the bladder. As it fills up, the bladder expands like a balloon.

When it's full, nerve endings in the bladder wall send your brain a message telling you it's time to pee. The urine then flows out of the body through the urethra.

When you go to the doctor, they often ask for a urine sample, because it can show how well your kidneys are working. Urine with white blood cells can be a sign of an infection. Urine with glucose can be a sign of diabetes. If your pee is a dark shade of yellow, it might just mean you need to drink more water.

Healthy kidneys prevent toxins from building up, regulate blood pressure, and help maintain the balance of water and salt in your body. They make sure your blood keeps everything it needs, and gets rid of anything it doesn't.

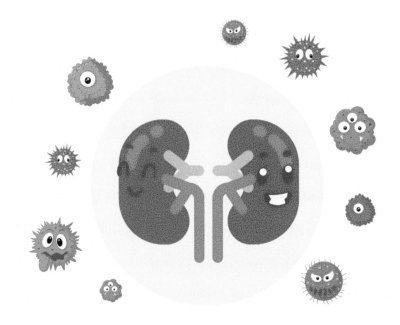

I Can Pee Clearly Now

Whenever you eat or drink something, your body separates it into nutrition and waste. The nutrition is kept in your body and used for energy, and the waste is sent out as urine or feces, otherwise known as poop.

For most healthy people, urine tends to be light yellow when they are well hydrated. When you get dehydrated, the color turns darker yellow, meaning that there is a higher concentration of waste in less water. That's a good sign that your kidneys are at work. It's also a signal that your body might want more water soon. Pay attention to how the color of your urine changes with how much water you're drinking.

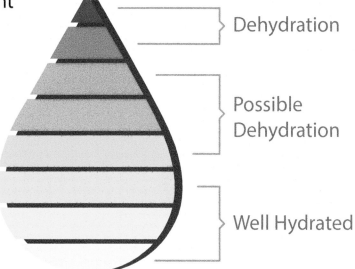

Dehydration

Possible Dehydration

Well Hydrated

Dr B.'s Note

The caffeine in sodas and energy drinks acts like a **diuretic**, which means that it makes your kidneys excrete even more water than usual. Next thing you know... you're thirsty AGAIN!

Urine Trouble

But You'll Pee Alright

As your urinary bladder fills up, it sends signals to your brain to tell you that you need to 'go.' That feeling is actually your body holding the urine inside your bladder by squeezing a **sphincter***. Sphincters are rings of muscle that control the opening and closing of tubes in your body, such as the urethra.

When you pee, your body is sending urine from the bladder out through your urethra, past the first sphincter. When this first sphincter opens, urine travels down the urethra until it reaches the final gate, the second sphincter. You control the opening or closing of this sphincter, which is why you can "hold your pee" until you find a toilet.

*Say it like this:

sphincter - "SFINK-ter"

The strongest syllable is always shown in CAPITALS and red.

Just because you CAN "hold your pee" does not mean you SHOULD hold it for too long!

Keeping a lot of urine in your bladder for a long time can lead to infections. Urine sitting around is a great place for bacteria to grow. When you start doing "the pee dance", you are trying to distract your bladder muscles from squeezing out urine. This means that you have been holding your urine for too long and should go to the bathroom right away!

Know When to Go

Now that you know all about how the kidneys filter out waste, let's examine what happens when the bladder is ready to expel excess water. We'll use home inventory materials to demonstrate. When the bladder gets full and the brain has signaled it is the right time to empty, urine moves out of the bladder through the urethra.

Materials:

- **A balloon or two** (in case one gets too full)
- **Water**
- **Straw**

Directions:

1. Fill a balloon with water (outside or over a sink) and hold the opening.

2. Place a straw inside the balloon, holding the opening still and placing a finger over the top of the straw.

3. Now over a sink or outside, remove your finger from the top opening of the straw and press all the water out of the balloon.

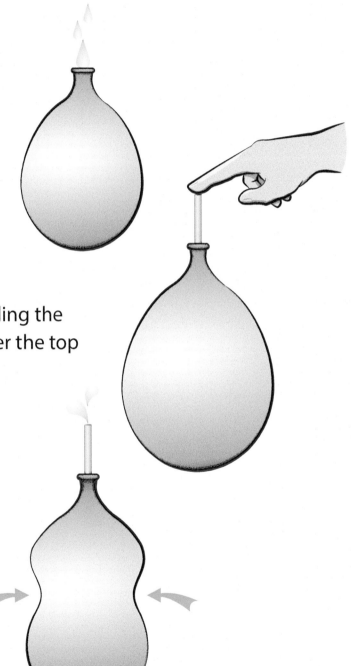

Homeostasis: Embrace This!

Your body has a very important way of keeping your water in **homeostasis*** (the right balance of your body's systems) — this is where your **renal* system** comes in. Renal means "having to do with the kidneys." You might know that you have two kidneys and that they are super important because they make urine. So they help you keep the water you need, while getting rid of the water and the wastes that you don't! Getting rid of wastes is called **excretion***. The kidneys work with some other big structures in the renal system to do this.

Your kidneys are found on either side of your spine, just between your lowest ribs. Each kidney is a little smaller than your fist.

***Say them like this:**

homeostasis - "home-ee-oh-STAY-sis"
renal - "REE-null"
excretion - "ex-CREE-shun"

The strongest syllable is always shown in CAPITALS and red.

Your kidneys also help keep your blood cells in homeostasis. When your body needs more blood cells, your kidneys make a chemical that tells your bone marrow to produce more.

Just like blood transports oxygen and nutrients to your organs, blood also carries waste away from your organs. Your kidneys are involved in two important jobs:

1) **To help the body absorb what it needs from your blood.**

2) **To filter waste and get it out of your body in the form of urine.**

Blood enters the kidneys by way of the renal arteries. Inside, blood flows through **nephrons,*** cleaning/filtration units made of capsules, tubes, and blood vessels. Each kidney has a million nephrons!

The nephrons take blood through a long roller coaster of tubes in the kidneys. This allows time for the body to reabsorb the things it needs and filter out the things it doesn't (waste, salts, and excess water — these are excreted as urine).

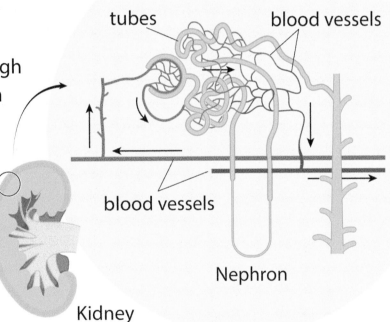

tubes   blood vessels

blood vessels

Nephron

Kidney

*Say it like this:

nephrons - "NEH-fronz"

The strongest syllable is always shown in CAPITALS and red.

The Renal System:
A River Runs Through Us

About 60% of your body is water.
You are more water than you are solid!

You have water:

- inside your cells (the building blocks of your body)
- in your tissues
- in your blood

All of this water helps:

- your body stay at the right temperature
- move nutrients where they need to go
- keep your moving parts from getting stuck together
- get rid of waste

To put it simply,
your body needs water to survive.

Water is your most essential nutrient, but you can lose up to 2 liters a day through sweating, breating, and getting rid of wastes in form of urine (often known as "pee") and feces (often known as "poop").

It's very important that you drink water to replace what you lose. Your body also does not want to have too much water, so it has ways to keep the right balance.

Keeping your body's stable is called **homeostasis**.

Hydration Station

Along with eating healthy meals and staying physically active, drinking enough water is an important habit to develop and maintain. But how much water is enough? The actual amounts change depending on your gender, height, weight, and lifestyle, but a good general rule is "8x8." Drink 8 cups of water (64 ounces) every day, and drink more if you're doing a lot of exercise or sweating.

A cup in this case isn't the same as the glass you're using to drink, but it's actually a measurement meaning 8 ounces which is the cup measurement used for cooking or baking. We'll figure out how much you're drinking with some quick math.

Materials:

- **Measuring cup**
- **Glass or cup for drinking**
- **Water**

Directions:

1. Fill the measuring cup with water and then dump it into the drinking cup. Repeat this until the drinking cup is mostly full.

2. Mark down how many cups went into your glass.

3. Use that same glass or cup throughout the day to drink water, and mark down every time you finish drinking.

4. At the end of each day, add up the marks and then multiply that number by the amount of measuring cups that you wrote down in step 2. Then multiply that number by 8, and write that down next to "oz" to track the total number of ounces of water you drank that day.

5. Practice this for two weeks and see how many days you can make the 64 oz goal! You might not hit your goal the first week, but it's important to keep trying!

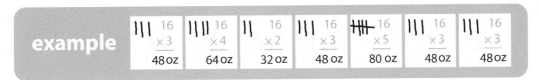

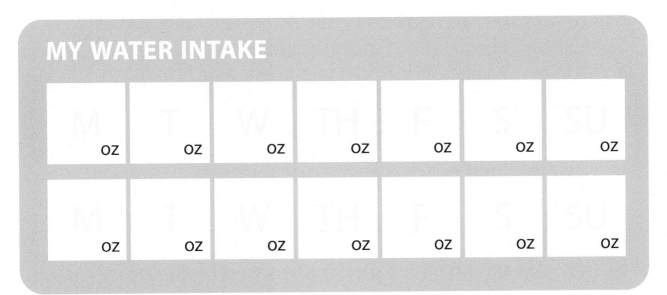

Potent Processor

Your kidneys work together to help your body absorb what it needs and get rid of what it doesn't, but for this game, we're going to pit them against each other!

Materials:

- **A copy of the Potent Processor Game Board**
- **5 tokens for each player**
- **1 6-sided die**

Directions:

1. Place 5 tokens at the start position for each player.

2. The youngest player goes first.

3. On each player's turn they can choose a single activity:
   - Move a token forward 2 spaces
   - Challenge your opponent to a game of Rock, Paper, Scissors, and if you win, roll the die. You can move a token forward the number of spaces shown on the die.
   - Move a piece from the bladder back to start.

4. When a piece makes it to the kidney, it triggers a game of Rock, Paper, Scissors.
   - If the player who wins controls the token, it gets absorbed by the body! Delicious nutrients!
   - If the player who wins doesn't control the token, the kidneys filter it and the piece goes to the bladder.

5. **The first player who gets 3 pieces absorbed by the body wins.**

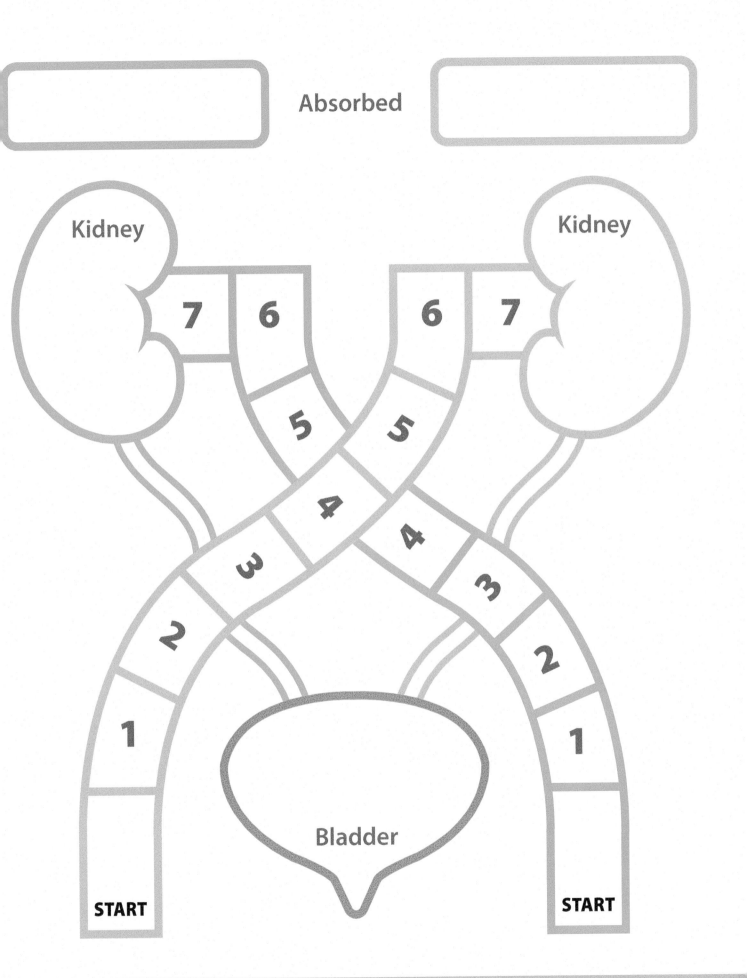

Absorbed

Kidney

Kidney

7 6 6 7

5 5

4 4

3 3

2 2

1 1

Bladder

START START

Renal Rumble

All the components of your renal system have gotten jumbled up! Find them to get things flowing.

BLADDER

BLOOD

FILTER

HYDRATION

KIDNEY

NEPHRONS

RENAL

TOXIN

URETERS

URETHRA

URINE

WATER

Answer keys on page 112.

```
T  K  U  R  K  N  C  P  X  R  O  H  N  C  I
O  Y  R  S  R  I  E  P  E  B  L  O  O  D  X
X  S  E  E  Y  E  D  D  U  X  W  Z  P  G  I
I  N  T  M  D  F  D  N  S  R  X  O  G  W  V
N  A  E  M  L  A  O  H  E  B  I  F  C  H  F
W  F  R  N  L  N  E  J  M  Y  M  N  Z  B  I
F  C  S  B  E  C  Z  Q  G  L  W  S  E  A  L
H  Y  U  E  Z  P  P  T  X  N  H  G  W  J  T
R  M  M  Z  Y  U  H  J  X  O  Y  F  U  B  E
H  R  B  I  L  T  K  R  T  C  G  Y  L  D  R
A  N  F  J  N  O  V  T  O  Y  C  A  Z  D  M
H  Y  D  R  A  T  I  O  N  N  N  K  Q  X  H
U  R  E  T  H  R  A  T  J  E  S  P  W  Q  I
C  L  Y  K  C  B  N  Q  R  R  M  W  A  H  N
H  K  T  T  Y  P  U  E  Q  A  L  K  G  H  J
```

Kidneys' Claim to Fame!

Now that you have learned all about the renal system, let's put your knowledge to the test!

Fill in the blanks below.

Your renal system is also known as the u__ __ __ __ __ __ system. In the renal

system, your kidneys are doing important work by disposing of w__ __ __ __ __

and carrying nutrients back to the h__ __ __ __ and the rest of your body.

It does this using 2 tube-like u__ __ __ __ __ __ , 1 elastic bladder,

and your urethra.

Inside the kidneys, n__ __ __ __ __ __ __ are the cleaning and filtration units

of the blood. You have m__ __ __ __ __ __ __ of nephrons! They help maintain

a healthy balance of n__ __ __ __ __ __ __ __ which get reabsorbed by

the b__ __ __ __ and kick out any wastes to the bladder.

The b___ ___ ___ ___ ___ is responsible for the storing of urine.

Once the bladder is full of wastes and excess water (known as urine or "p___ ___"),

you may feel a strong sensation. A full bladder sends a signal to the nervous

system that it needs to be emptied soon through your u___ ___ ___ ___ ___ ___.

Without the outstanding work of the kidneys, you would get s___ ___ ___

very quickly!

The kidney bean was named after the look

and shape of real k___ ___ ___ ___ ___ ___.

This is just 1 more reason why

the kidneys are a famous organ!

Ready to verify what you have learned?
See the answer key on page 113!

Know Your Appetite

Experience Assyrian Foods

Assyrians are credited with creating the first written recipes, dating back to the 18th century BCE. Written on clay tablets, their recipes most likely featured chickpeas, dates, barley, and a paste from toasted, ground sesame seeds called tahini. In fact, we know that people in the region of the Assyrian Empire have been eating chickpeas since before there was pottery!

Assyrians lived in a hot, rocky part of the world. They needed foods that were portable, flavorful, and high in protein, minerals, and vitamins. We've included two recipes inspired by the Assyrian lifestyle.

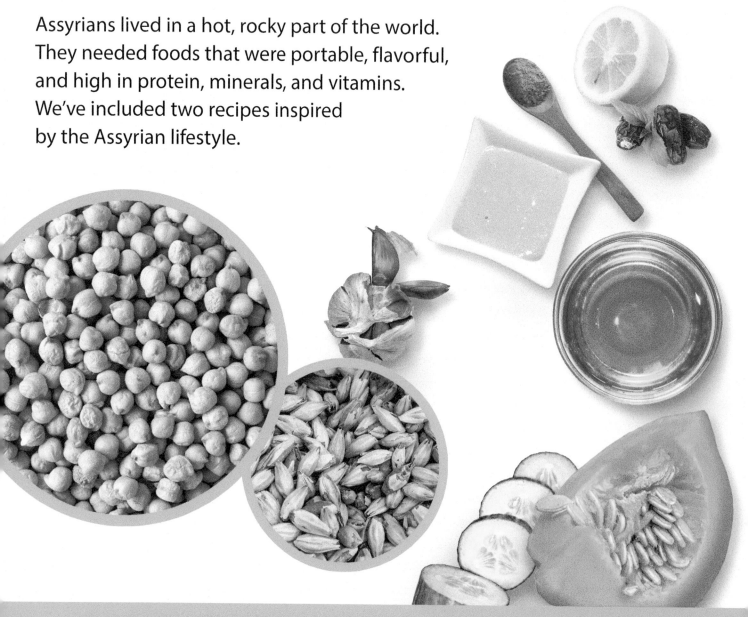

Pinky's Hint:

Read through the entire recipe before beginning to prepare food. This way, you'll know what equipment and ingredients are needed, and you'll be familiar with the steps involved.

Whenever you see the chef's hat icon, it means **you'll need an adult's help**.

Using the alphabet guide on page 33, decipher this message:

_____ __ _____ ___ __ ___ _ ___ __

Recipes and food knowledge provided by
Chef Polly Legendre of La Gourmande Catering.

Tahini Hummus

The name "hummus" comes from the Arabic word for chickpeas, which were a staple food of ancient Assyria. Chickpeas have a high concentration of iron, a mineral that your body needs to make red blood cells.

A good meal could consist of lentils, boiled millet, barley prepared as we prepare rice, and possibly maize. Common vegetables and fruit used by the Assyrians were pumpkins, cucumbers, and melons. Fish was a popular source of protein, and was readily available in the rivers flowing through Assyria.

**Prep time:
10 minutes**

Ingredients:

- 1 can (15 ounces) of chickpeas (garbanzo beans), drained
- 1/4 cup tahini (sesame paste)
- 1 clove of garlic, smashed
- 1 lemon, juiced
- 1/4 teaspooon salt
- 1/2 cup olive oil

Preparation:

1. In a food processor or blender, combine the chickpeas with the garlic, tahini, lemon juice, and salt. Mix it until it becomes a thick paste. You can add a little water if necessary to help with the blending.

2. Add the olive oil and then mix again until it becomes smooth.

3. Be sure to scrape down the sides of the blender so that no big chunks are left.

4. Serve the hummus with pita bread and vegetables, or use it as a tasty spread on your favorite sandwich.

 Show off your cooking skills!

Have your grown up take a photo, and share on social media using the hashtag:

#KnowYourAdventure

 KnowYourselfOAK 　　f KnowYourselfOAK

Walnut Butter Cookies

Assyrians sweetened their food with date syrup, but honey is another simple, healthy option.

Prep time:
5 to 10 minutes

Cooking time:
18 minutes

Makes 20–22 cookies

Ingredients:

- 1/4 cup sugar

- 1 cup all-purpose flour

- 3/4 cup shelled walnuts (for dough)

- 1 stick of butter at room temperature

- 1/2 teaspoon ground cardamom

- 1/8 teaspoon salt

- 2 tablespoons date syrup or honey

- 20 to 22 walnuts halves (for cookie tops)

Preparation:

1. Pre-heat your oven to 325 degrees.

 2. Combine sugar, flour, 3/4 cup shelled walnuts, butter, cardamom and salt in a food processor. Use the pulse setting to mix all the ingredients together until it looks like chunky, wet sand.

3. Add the 2 tablespoons of date syrup or honey, then continue to mix until the dough starts to hold together.

4. Roll the dough into balls, about 2 teaspoons at a time. Place the balls on a greased cookie sheet about 1 inch apart.

5. Place a piece of walnut on the top of each ball, pushing it down into the dough just a little.

 6. Bake the cookies for 18 minutes or until golden brown.

7. Cool cookies completely before removing them from the pan. Enjoy with family and friends!

Thoughts for Young Chefs

What did you learn about Assyrian food that you didn't know before this Adventure?

_____

_____

_____

_____

_____

_____

 Show off your cooking skills!

Have your grown up take a photo,
and share on social media using the hashtag:

#KnowYourAdventure

 KnowYourselfOAK   KnowYourselfOAK

Know Yourself Adventure Recipes

Review the recipes from this adventure and what you eat.
Record similarities and differences in the Venn Diagram below.

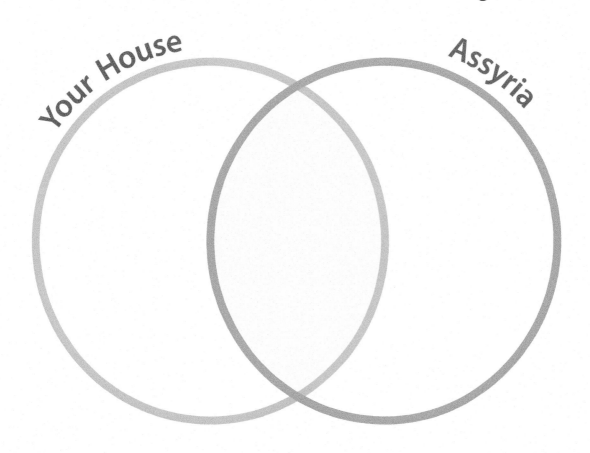

What type of food are you inspired to make next?

_____

_____

_____

Babble On About Babylon

Great work finishing this Adventure Guide!

Before you end your journey, take a moment to ponder a few last questions below (or 'babble-on' about Babylon)!

In this adventure, you learned about the Hanging Gardens of Babylon and the renal system. You found out how the gardens were watered through an irrigation system, and how inside your body our urinary system helps expel waste and excess water from the body.

How do these two compare?

_____

_____

_____

_____

_____

_____

Now that you have learned about your renal system. What are some things you can do to help your renal system stay healthy?

_____

_____

_____

_____

_____

_____

_____

_____

_____

Babble On About Babylon

(continuation)

On page 46, you created your own mythical creature. **How much water do you think they need to drink a day to stay hydrated? Why?**

_____

_____

_____

_____

_____

_____

_____

_____

_____

Ancient Assyria is known for its firsts in activities such as writing, banking and geometry. Just like your body has systems like the renal system to keep everything working, **how do you think these advancements contributed to Assyrian civilization?**

_____

_____

_____

_____

_____

_____

_____

_____

THE SEVENTH SENSE

Further Reading

Nonfiction for Younger Readers

In this book, readers take a deeper dive into learning about the many parts in the urinary and digestive systems. The book uses character illustrations to present the body system for a visual learning experience.

The Digestive and Urinary Systems
Midthun, Joseph and Hiti, Samuel; Ages 7-10

Nonfiction for Older Readers

This is a great resource for students who would like to learn more about Ancient Mesopotamia. The book covers social organization, important people and architecture during this period.

Ancient Mesopotamia - Sumerians, Babylonians, Assyrians
Schomp, Virginia; Ages 11-13

Further Reading

Nonfiction for All Ages

- *Britannica Kids*

  For students looking for more information that is adaptable to their reading level or interest level, Britannica Kids offers two levels of information covering Babylon and the Assyrian Empire. When accessing the website, you can select the depth of material provided by choosing either "Kids" or "Students" on the top right of the article.

  https://kids.britannica.com/kids/article/Babylonia-and-Assyria/352812

- *Kids Health*

  Kids Health was founded with the goal of helping families better understand their health, and this article provides some additional fun information about kidneys. It's a good start for those looking to learn more.

  https://kidshealth.org/en/kids/kidneys.html

5 NEXT
The Digestive System

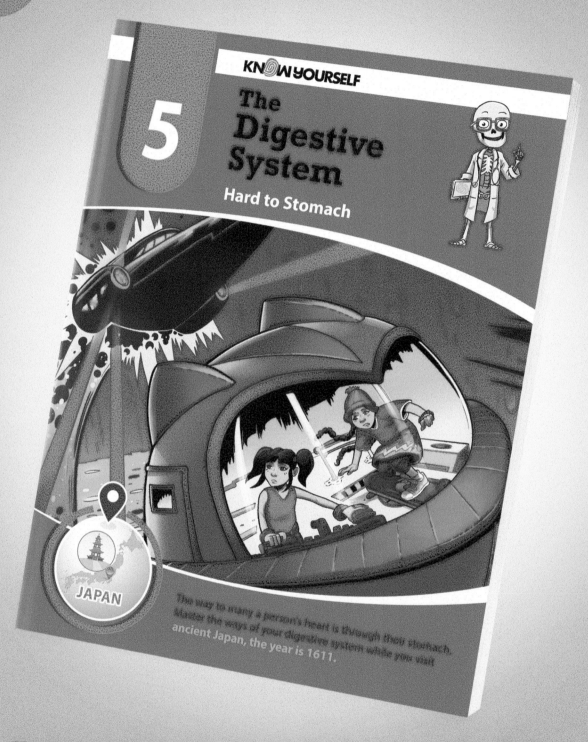

KN♥W YOURSELF

5

The Digestive System

Hard to Stomach

JAPAN

The way to many a person's heart is through their stomach. Master the ways of your digestive system while you visit ancient Japan, the year is 1611.

The way to many a person's heart is through their stomach. Master the ways of your digestive system while you visit ancient Japan, the year is 1611... it's HARD TO STOMACH!

Get to Know...

Shorty Lemonade

Gifted with a special ability to motivate other kids to work together, Shorty is an expert leader. In one word, she is BOSS (but not bossy). You can often find Shorty picking
lemons from her grandmother's lemon tree in West Oakland and listening to her grandmother's incredible stories — and now she can do that with her super-hearing!

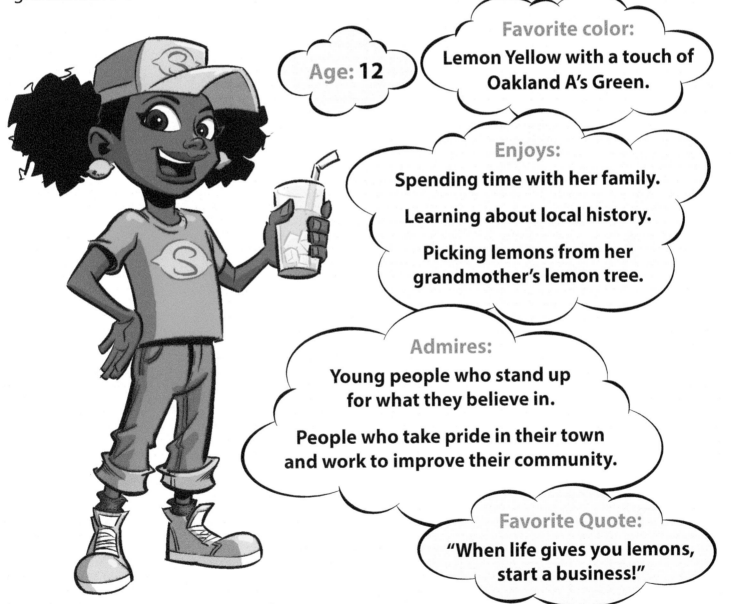

Age: 12

Favorite color:
Lemon Yellow with a touch of Oakland A's Green.

Enjoys:

Spending time with her family.

Learning about local history.

Picking lemons from her grandmother's lemon tree.

Admires:

Young people who stand up for what they believe in.

People who take pride in their town and work to improve their community.

Favorite Quote:
"When life gives you lemons, start a business!"

Ancient Assyria Crossword

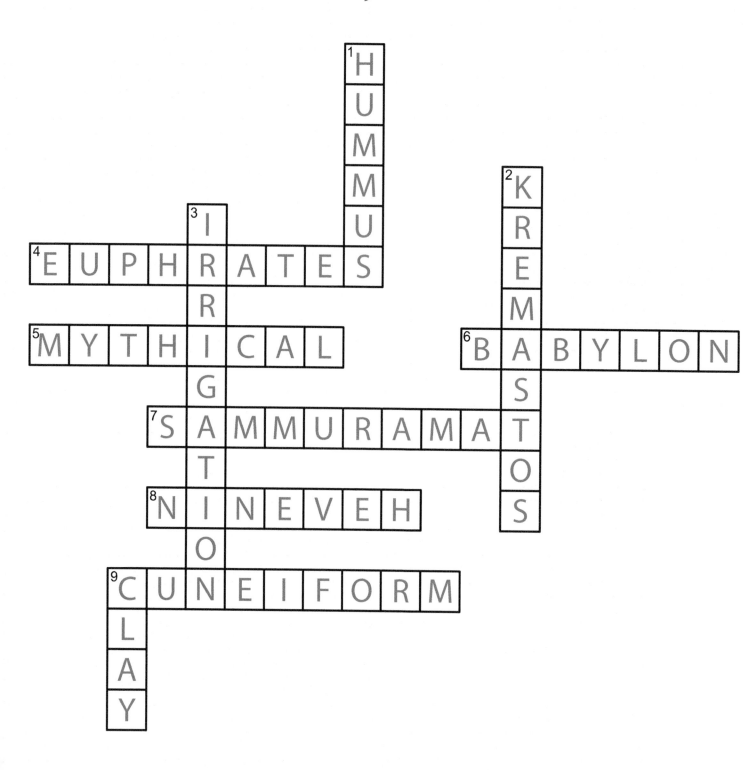

Don't Make a Mess(opotamia)

Ancient Assyria is very old, and historians believe it may have been the first place

we know of where people studied g e o m e t r y , had advanced

b a n k i n g and even had a common system for w r i t i n g

used for things like recipes.

Mesopotamia means "the country between two rivers," because it was located

between the T i g r i s and the E u p h r a t e s .

The city of Babylon was known for many things, but perhaps the most famous are

"The H a n g i n g G a r d e n s of Babylon", which were listed

among "The S e v e n Wonders of the Ancient world," though now historians

aren't sure if they were more history or myth.

Queen S a m m u – R a m a t was one of the world's first known female

rulers, serving as the empress of Assyria until her s o n could take over. Accord-

ing to legends, she was responsible for many c o n s t r u c t i o n

projects, the remnants of which are a large part of how Assyria is studied today!

Answer Keys

Renal Rumble

```
T K U R K N C P X R O H N C I
O Y R S R I E P E B L O O D X
X S E E Y E D D U X W Z P G I
I N T M D F D N S R X O G W V
N A E M L A O H E B I F C H F
W F R N L N E J M Y M N Z B I
F C S B E C Z Q G L W S E A L
H Y U E Z P P T X N H G W J T
R M M Z Y U H J X O Y F U B E
H R B I L T K R T C G Y L D R
A N F J N O V T O Y C A Z D M
H Y D R A T I O N N N K Q X H
U R E T H R A T J E S P W Q I
C L Y K C B N Q R R M W A H N
H K T T Y P U E Q A L K G H J
```

Kidneys' Claim to Fame

Your renal system is also known as the u r i n a r y system. In the renal

system, your kidneys are doing important work by disposing of w a s t e s

and carrying nutrients back to the h e a r t and the rest of your body.

It does this using 2 tube-like u r e t e r s , 1 elastic bladder,

and your urethra.

Inside the kidneys, n e p h r o n s are the cleaning and filtration units

of the blood. You have m i l l i o n s of nephrons! They help maintain

a healthy balance of n u t r i e n t s which get reabsorbed by

the b l o o d and kick out any wastes to the bladder.

The b l a d d e r is responsible for the storing of urine.

Once the bladder is full of wastes and excess water (known as urine or "p e e "),

you may feel a strong sensation. A full bladder sends a signal to the nervous

system that it needs to be emptied soon through your u r e t h r a .

Without the outstanding work of the kidneys, you would get s i c k

very quickly!

The kidney bean was named after the look and shape of real k i d n e y s .

This is just 1 more reason why the kidneys are a famous organ!

CREATED WITH LOVE
BY THE
KNOW YOURSELF TEAM